Contents

❶ Key features of Abacus

The Abacus programme

Abacus follows the detailed plan of teaching objectives outlined in the Framework for Teaching Mathematics. Furthermore, Abacus, from its inception, has been designed and written with precisely the same approach to the teaching of mathematics as that of the National Numeracy Strategy. Abacus is based on three principles:

Direct and interactive teaching is at the heart of the process of helping children learn mathematics. Children often do not 'discover' strategies; they have to be taught them.

Many mathematical skills and facts, particularly those which help children become fluent in mental calculations, need to be taught clearly, and then rehearsed regularly on a 'little-and-often' basis.

Materials need to support teachers in their teaching, and to help keep classroom management simple and effective. It is not necessary, nor is it desirable, for every classroom teacher to 'reinvent the wheel'. A clear structure of key objectives (with sufficient flexibility for important professional decisions to be left to each teacher in their own specific context) will minimise the hours spent planning and preparing, and maximise the teacher's effectiveness in the classroom.

As well as being based on the same philosophy, Abacus shares several assumptions with the National Numeracy Strategy.

- There will be a daily mathematics lesson.
- The lesson will have a three-part structure. Although the timing will be flexible, and will vary from lesson to lesson, class to class and school to school, the key elements will be common to all years and to all classroom contexts.
- Planning will be carried out on a weekly basis, with reference to the medium term planning grids in the Framework for Teaching Mathematics.
- In their direct teaching, with the whole class, in groups or with individuals and pairs, teachers will require simple practical resources. These will include large number lines, large number grids, medium number lines and small number grids, pupil sets of digit cards and place-value cards.

❷ The National Numeracy Strategy

The National context

The National Numeracy Strategy follows the recommendations of the final report of the Numeracy Task Force (1998) that throughout the primary phase in education there should be:

● a daily mathematics lesson of 45 to 60 minutes
● a greatly increased proportion of whole class interactive direct teaching of mathematics
● a focus on teaching mental calculation strategies.

At the heart of the National Numeracy Strategy is the Framework for Teaching Mathematics. This document provides a structured sequence of teaching objectives for each school year. Put simply, it outlines the mathematical content which must be taught to each year group. Teachers are wholly aware of the necessity for teaching a structured sequence of skills to children, particularly in relation to developing effective mental calculation strategies (we are all familiar with the problem of teaching a topic, only to find that an essential pre-requisite skill has not been covered). The Framework provides just such a programme. From September 1999, all schools in England will be expected either to draw upon the Framework for Teaching Mathematics in planning their lessons, or to ensure that their teaching programme covers a similarly complete and structured sequence of teaching objectives, with a focus on the development of mental calculation strategies.

The three-part lesson

In the National Numeracy Strategy and in Abacus, the daily mathematics lesson has the following three-part structure.

Part of lesson	What it comprises	Content includes	Abacus resources
Oral/ mental starter	Usually number work Sometimes related directly to the main teaching activity and sometimes not.	Counting (in steps of 1000, 50, 0.1, 0.5 etc.) Strategies which have already been taught Number facts (+, −, ×, ÷)	*Mental Warm-up Activities* *Simmering Activities*
Main teaching activity	One of the following: Whole class introduction to the topic, using some paired work Group work Paired investigations Individual practice	Selected objectives from an appropriate year of the Framework for Teaching Mathematics	*Teacher Cards* *Activity Books* *Workbooks* *Photocopy Masters*
Plenary	Validation and report on the work of children with whom you haven't worked directly Rehearsal of main teaching objective in the light of any common misconceptions Explanation of the content to be covered next	Summary of key objectives Outline of objectives to be addressed next Reinforcement activity Possible homework activity	*Teacher Cards* *Simmering Activities* *Homework Books*

There is a variety of possible formats for the middle part of the lesson, depending on:

- where in the particular topic the lesson takes place (e.g. introducing a topic, continuing or extending a topic, assessing a topic, or revising a topic)
- the nature of the mathematical topic being taught
- the age and maturity of the children
- the nature of the classroom and school (e.g. mixed-age class, small rural school, large urban school, special school or unit).

The three-part structure is flexible, and is designed to accommodate teacher's individual teaching styles as well as differences in situation, organisation and content.

It is assumed (by the National Numeracy Strategy and by Abacus) that at the start of a topic there will be more whole class teaching, whereas in the middle or towards the end of a topic, there will be more teaching, focused on groups, pairs or individuals. However, over the topic as a whole, there will be a substantial proportion of direct teaching of the whole class (or of the whole year group in mixed-age classes).

❸ Classroom management

The Teacher Card

For each unit of work the Teacher Card identifies for you:
- the direct teaching (introductory and follow-up) to the whole class or group
- whole class activities and small group differentiated activities
- appropriate Photocopy Masters, Workbook pages and Mental Warm-up Activities
- ideas for Plenaries.

This enables you to plan effectively for the whole class (large or small), covering a wide range of ability.

Children will experience a range of tasks within each unit, the actual composition determined by you, following the guidance on the Teacher Card.

Classroom organisation

Abacus allows for flexibility in the organisation of the children. On the assumption that the teaching takes place with the whole class, this can be followed using a variety of different organisational structures. Examples include:
- the whole class working together on the same activity, possibly in pairs
- half of the class working on one Activity, whilst the other half work on another Activity
- a 'carousel' of Activities, with the children in groups, moving from one activity to another
- half of the children working in groups on Activities, whilst the other half are working on material in the Workbooks or Photocopy Masters.

Organising groups

- You will decide on the best organisation of groups to suit your needs at any time. There should be no more than three levels of work in a single-age class and no more than four in a mixed-age class.
- The composition of the groups will vary depending on the unit of work being studied.
- You can plan within your group structure, how, during the unit, you can work in a focused way with any one group.
- You will need to judge how much time to allow for different children to complete any task. The carousel nature of the tasks provides versatility in management.
- Other adults can be used to assist with the activities.
- Some children in the class may be used occasionally in a peer-tutoring role within the activity carousel.

4 The Abacus materials

Mental Warm-up Activities

The Mental Warm-up Activities Book provides a comprehensive scheme of work for developing mental mathematics strategies. Each day you will select an appropriate activity to take place before the main part of the lesson. The activities are designed to rehearse and sharpen key mental mathematics skill, including counting, comparing and ordering numbers. They allow you to get off to a clear, crisp start to the lesson.

The Reception Mental Warm-up Activities are arranged under topic headings, e.g. Birthday maths, Rhymes, Counting songs. They practise basic skills in a style accessible to young children. Some of the activities will become favourites that children will want to return to throughout the year.

F3 Bossyboot numbers

To recognise written numerals up to 9; to order consecutive numbers given in random order.
Number cards (0 to 9)

Give ten children a number card each and line them up 'in a muddle'.

The other children act as the 'Bossyboots', calling out instructions to one child at a time to put them in the correct order, e.g. *Jade, you need to move to the end of the line next to Latha and Jack, can you go and stand between Sonja and Jyoti?*

Children who find it difficult to say the instructions could come up and gently move children.

F4 What's my number?

To recognise written numerals up to 9
Wooden/plastic numbers

Choose children to come up to the front one by one. Turn them to face the other children, with their back to you.

Choose a number between 0 and 9 and 'draw' the number slowly and deliberately on their back with your finger, so that they can feel your finger tracing the outline. Can they guess what the number is?

Give them some help *It's got a round part, and a straight line right next to it* (9). *It's got a hook, and then a straight line across the bottom* (2).

If you have wooden/plastic numbers, the children can hold the number behind their back and feel it.

F5 Silly Teddy (counting problems)

To recite the number names in order to 40 and back; to suggest numbers which lie between two given numbers; to solve simple mathematical puzzles
A teddy bear

Tell the children that Silly Teddy has been learning to count and that you want them to listen to see how well he is doing.

You count for Teddy, stumbling and hesitating after a few numbers, e.g. *One, two, three... four, five, six, seven ...eight, nine ...ten, eleven, twelve, fourteen, fifteen, sixteen ...*

Oh no, Teddy missed out a number. Let's start from 10 and count with Teddy. Ten, eleven ... twenty.

Which number did Teddy miss out?

Repeat, missing out other numbers.

Repeat, but counting back from 10 or 20.

F6 Musical numbers

To recognise written numerals up to 9; to count reliably in contexts such as sounds (hand claps) or movements (hops); to order any set of four or five numbers given in random order; to order consecutive numbers given in random order
A tape player; a music tape; a bag; small number cards (1 to 20), one set

Put the number cards in a bag. Then sit everyone in a circle and play the music. The children pass the bag of numbers around the circle as the music plays.

When the music stops, the child holding the bag removes a card from the bag and reads it out. Can they hop that number of times? Then the number is placed in the middle of the circle on the floor. As more numbers are placed in the middle of the circle, encourage children to place them in the correct order, to create a number line.

Teacher Cards

The main teaching for the lesson is supported by the Teacher Cards.
The front of each Teacher Card provides:

- support for the whole class teaching on the first day of a topic
- a list of the key teaching points addressed by the Unit
- a list of any materials necessary for the teaching
- key vocabulary either introduced or used during the course of the Unit.

N2 Numbers to 10

Teaching points

- To recite the number names in order to 20
- To begin to count a set of objects up to 10, giving one number name to each object
- To begin to record numbers (up to 10)

Materials

- Large number line (1 to 20)
- 30 cubes (or use: grapes, savoury biscuits or raisins)
- Large dice (1 to 6)

Key words

- one ... ten
- count
- how many?
- correct
- up/down
- across
- round

Teaching

- Practise counting. Hold up one finger for each number. Start with the thumb on the left hand. *One, two, three, four, five.* Stress the *five*, shaking the hand with five upright fingers. Continue. Start with the thumb on the right hand, holding up one finger for each number spoken. *Six, seven, eight, nine, ten!* Shake both hands to emphasise the ten fingers.

- Repeat several times, and continue the count to 20 in the same way. Emphasise **fifteen** by shaking the left hand, and **twenty** by shaking both hands.

- Choose a child to throw the large dice. *What number have they thrown?* Ask everyone to count the spots together. *One, two, three...* Touch each spot on the dice as you count.

- Choose another child to find the matching number on the number line. Show how to write this number on the board. Stress where you start, and how to form the number, e.g. up, across, down, round and along the bottom etc. Choose several children to come and do this.

- Choose another child to count out that number of cubes. Count these in unison. *One, two, three...*

- Choose a different child to throw the dice. *How many have they thrown?* Count the spots in unison, pointing to each spot as you say the number. Choose another child to find the matching number on the line. Show how to write this number and ask several children to practise it on the board. Finally, choose a child to count out that number of cubes.

- Repeat, throwing the dice each time until everyone has had a go.

R N2

4. The Abacus materials

The back of each Teacher Card provides:
- support for further teaching for subsequent days
- references to differentiated practical activities, including materials and learning outcomes (which are presented in a separate Activity Book)
- guidance on key points, common misconceptions etc., for use during plenary sessions
- references to additional Abacus resources: Mental Warm-up Activities, Workbooks, Photocopy Masters.

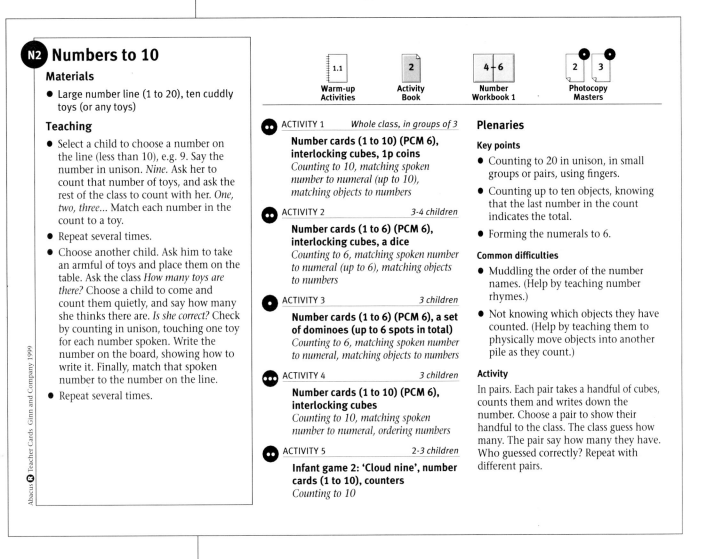

N2 Numbers to 10

Materials
- Large number line (1 to 20), ten cuddly toys (or any toys)

Teaching
- Select a child to choose a number on the line (less than 10), e.g. 9. Say the number in unison. *Nine.* Ask her to count that number of toys, and ask the rest of the class to count with her. *One, two, three...* Match each number in the count to a toy.
- Repeat several times.
- Choose another child. Ask him to take an armful of toys and place them on the table. Ask the class *How many toys are there?* Choose a child to come and count them quietly, and say how many she thinks there are. *Is she correct?* Check by counting in unison, touching one toy for each number spoken. Write the number on the board, showing how to write it. Finally, match that spoken number to the number on the line.
- Repeat several times.

Warm-up Activities 1.1

Activity Book 2

Number Workbook 1 4-6

Photocopy Masters 2 3

ACTIVITY 1 *Whole class, in groups of 3*
Number cards (1 to 10) (PCM 6), interlocking cubes, 1p coins
Counting to 10, matching spoken number to numeral (up to 10), matching objects to numbers

ACTIVITY 2 *3-4 children*
Number cards (1 to 6) (PCM 6), interlocking cubes, a dice
Counting to 6, matching spoken number to numeral (up to 6), matching objects to numbers

ACTIVITY 3 *3 children*
Number cards (1 to 6) (PCM 6), a set of dominoes (up to 6 spots in total)
Counting to 6, matching spoken number to numeral, matching objects to numbers

ACTIVITY 4 *3 children*
Number cards (1 to 10) (PCM 6), interlocking cubes
Counting to 10, matching spoken number to numeral, ordering numbers

ACTIVITY 5 *2-3 children*
Infant game 2: 'Cloud nine', number cards (1 to 10), counters
Counting to 10

Plenaries

Key points
- Counting to 20 in unison, in small groups or pairs, using fingers.
- Counting up to ten objects, knowing that the last number in the count indicates the total.
- Forming the numerals to 6.

Common difficulties
- Muddling the order of the number names. (Help by teaching number rhymes.)
- Not knowing which objects they have counted. (Help by teaching them to physically move objects into another pile as they count.)

Activity
In pairs. Each pair takes a handful of cubes, counts them and writes down the number. Choose a pair to show their handful to the class. The class guess how many. The pair say how many they have. Who guessed correctly? Repeat with different pairs.

Abacus ✱ Teacher Cards Ginn and Company 1999

The Teacher Cards are divided into two sets: *Number* and *Shape, Space and Measures*. A suggested teaching order, and how this fits with the National Numeracy Framework Planning Grids are given at the end of this book (from page 41). There are other possible routes through the materials, and the *Shape, Space and Measures* units are presented in a separate block to allow you easily to re-order them.

Activity Book

The Activity Book includes all the practical activities which will follow the introductory teaching. Each Unit of the programme is supported by a range of activities, covering different styles, learning objectives, numbers of children and resources, which are fully referenced on each Teacher Card. Most units include an Activity which may be taught to the whole class. Such activities are indicated by the icon:

Each activity includes the following information:
- appropriate number of children
- a list of relevant materials and 'specialist' resources (provided as Photocopy Masters at the back of the book)
- level of difficulty, indicated by a simple code: ● basic work, ●● for all children, ●●● enrichment and extension
- learning points are also provided. These will assist the teacher in directing the group and in making informal assessments.

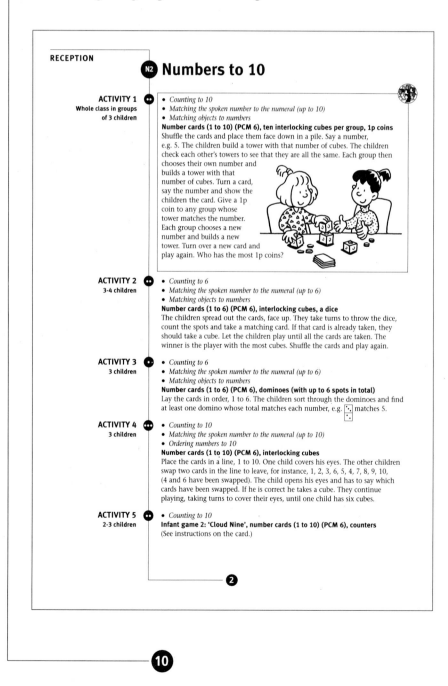

RECEPTION

N2 Numbers to 10

ACTIVITY 1 ●●
Whole class in groups
of 3 children
- *Counting to 10*
- *Matching the spoken number to the numeral (up to 10)*
- *Matching objects to numbers*
Number cards (1 to 10) (PCM 6), ten interlocking cubes per group, 1p coins
Shuffle the cards and place them face down in a pile. Say a number, e.g. 5. The children build a tower with that number of cubes. The children check each other's towers to see that they are all the same. Each group then chooses their own number and builds a tower with that number of cubes. Turn a card, say the number and show the children the card. Give a 1p coin to any group whose tower matches the number. Each group chooses a new number and builds a new tower. Turn over a new card and play again. Who has the most 1p coins?

ACTIVITY 2 ●●
3-4 children
- *Counting to 6*
- *Matching the spoken number to the numeral (up to 6)*
- *Matching objects to numbers*
Number cards (1 to 6) (PCM 6), interlocking cubes, a dice
The children spread out the cards, face up. They take turns to throw the dice, count the spots and take a matching card. If that card is already taken, they should take a cube. Let the children play until all the cards are taken. The winner is the player with the most cubes. Shuffle the cards and play again.

ACTIVITY 3 ●●
3 children
- *Counting to 6*
- *Matching the spoken number to the numeral (up to 6)*
- *Matching objects to numbers*
Number cards (1 to 6) (PCM 6), dominoes (with up to 6 spots in total)
Lay the cards in order, 1 to 6. The children sort through the dominoes and find at least one domino whose total matches each number, e.g. [∴·] matches 5.

ACTIVITY 4 ●●
3 children
- *Counting to 10*
- *Matching the spoken number to the numeral (up to 10)*
- *Ordering numbers to 10*
Number cards (1 to 10) (PCM 6), interlocking cubes
Place the cards in a line, 1 to 10. One child covers his eyes. The other children swap two cards in the line to leave, for instance, 1, 2, 3, 6, 5, 4, 7, 8, 9, 10, (4 and 6 have been swapped). The child opens his eyes and has to say which cards have been swapped. If he is correct he takes a cube. They continue playing, taking turns to cover their eyes, until one child has six cubes.

ACTIVITY 5 ●●
2-3 children
- *Counting to 10*
Infant game 2: 'Cloud Nine', number cards (1 to 10) (PCM 6), counters
(See instructions on the card.)

2

Workbooks

There are four Workbooks in Abacus R, three for *Number* and one for *Shape, Space and Measures*. Each Workbook page offers consolidation of the practical work covered by you and gives evidence of the children's progress through the scheme.

On each page, the relevant Abacus Unit is identified, along with a heading, which highlights the mathematical content of the page and reinforces key vocabulary. A key feature of the pages is the inclusion of 'Extras' (coded ❷), which provide additional activities usually with an investigational or practical focus away from the Workbook page. Relevant Workbook pages are referenced on each Teacher Card.

Photocopy Masters

The Photocopy Masters contain activities to enhance the children's learning and are identified on the relevant Teacher Cards. They include:
● more work for reinforcement
● extension and enrichment material
● games, and other shared, practical activities.

The Photocopy Masters are coded in the same way as the practical activities: ● basic work, ●● for all children, ●● enrichment and extension.

Resource Bank and Infant Games

The Resource Bank provides the essential materials needed for the teaching and practical activities in the programme. The basic resources you need for Reception are recommended on page 34, but the Resource Bank gives you the flexibility to order additional sets of materials to suit your particular needs. Items include: group and class sets of number cards, place-value cards, wall charts and number line cards.

The Infant Games pack provides 24 games aimed at practising skills relating to specific Teacher Card units. They are included as activities in the Activity Book.

Simmering Activities

Relevant rhymes, quick-recalls, games and other activities are contained in the Simmering Activities book. The activities require little or no preparation and are brief enough to be carried out in just a few minutes – at registration or in the dinner queue. Once introduced, the activity can be used regularly to allow the concept or skill to keep 'simmering'.

Section 1: Counting to 10

Abacus R
N1, N2, N5, N7, N8,
N9, N10, N13, N14,
N15, N17, N18, N20, N21

Abacus 1
N1, N2, N7, N15,
N24, N29, N36

- **Three, two, one, blast off!**
  With the children sitting, count in unison slowly and clearly up to ten and back from ten.
  On the way down the children get ready to jump: ...*three, two, one, blast off*. The children jump up in the air like a rocket taking off.
  Repeat this activity often – at least twice a day for a while. Children gain immensely from counting in unison like this.
  Extend to counting to twenty when the children are ready.

- **Pinned on me!**
  Paper and pencil, sticky tape
  Write a number between 1 and 10 and stick it to a child's back so the other children can see it. They give the first child clues about the number without using its name. For example, they may say 'It's less than 5' or 'It's only got straight lines' or 'It's Jo's favourite number'.
  How quickly can the first child guess the number? Repeat with another child.

- **Finger count-up**
  This is a good activity for an assembly. Count in unison to ten, holding up one finger for each number spoken, so at *ten* all ten fingers are standing up. Then count down from ten, folding down one finger for each number spoken. Practise doing this quickly. How fast can the class count? Co-ordinating fingers with counting is difficult, and takes practice.

- **Target number**
  Ask the children to sit in a circle. Agree a target number, e.g. 7. Count around the circle from one, children taking turns to say a number. When ten is reached, start counting again at one. Any child who says the target number must stand up. Continue until five children are standing.

- **Quack, quack...**
  Ask the children to sit in a circle. The children take turns to choose an animal and make the appropriate number of noises. For example, the first child quacks once, the second child miaows twice, the third child barks three times, and so on up to ten.
  Count down from ten in the same way. Ensure everyone has a turn. The children can suggest animals.

- **One more or one less**
  Ask the children to sit in pairs and tell them stories involving 'one less' or 'one more'. For example:
  Five big, hairy spiders march across the teacher's desk. One falls on the floor. How many are still on the desk?
  There were three big, muddy puddles. Tom fell in one and sat down! Amy fell in the other and sat down! How many puddles are left?

- **Counting songs**
  Sing counting songs with the children. Encourage the children to use their fingers to represent the numbers in these songs.

  Once I caught a fish alive
  One, two, three, four, five
  Once I caught a fish alive
  Six, seven, eight, nine, ten
  Then I let it go again

  Why did I let it go?
  Because it bit my finger so
  Which finger did it bite?
  This little finger on my right.

  One man went to mow
  One man went to mow
  Went to mow a meadow
  One man and his dog, Spot,
  Went to mow a meadow.

1

2

⑤ An Abacus Unit

Abacus was conceived with the identical approach to teaching as the National Numeracy Strategy. The New Abacus unit matches precisely the structure of a sequence of linked three-part lessons through a topic. As an illustration, the planning for a typical Year 2 lesson (adding 2-digit numbers mentally) is shown below.

	Day 1	Day 2	Day 3
Mental/oral starter	Practise a necessary pre-requisite skill, e.g. counting in tens	Rehearse number bonds to ten to help with quick arithmetic	Play a 'bingo' game, adding 11 and 12 to 2-digit numbers
Main teaching activity	1. Introduce topic to whole class, using a large number grid (1 to 100) as a model and demonstrating how to add multiples of ten and then add units, e.g. $34 + 23 = 34 + 20 + 3$. 2. Children all do brief practice activity in workbooks, teacher working with least able group.	1. Briefly rehearse the main teaching point, teaching using the number grid. 2. Children work in 4 groups. Teacher works with less able children, providing a hands-on activity and further teaching. 'Middle' two groups work independently on written practice. More able children work on an extension activity.	1. Rehearse the main point, using a different model (e.g. 10p and 1p coins, place-value cards). 2. Children work in pairs and individually on a graded task using money and/or place-value cards as appropriate, and recording their work in their mathematics book. 3. Assess children's work, looking at how far they progressed with graded task
Plenary	Rehearse the main point and play a game to practise the method.	Feedback from middle two groups and more able to whole class. Address some common difficulties.	Rehearse main teaching point through common difficulty. Summarise what the children have learned.

5. An Abacus Unit

Immediately it is clear that the Abacus materials have been designed to fit the structure shown in the above topic plan.

	Day 1	Day 2	Day 3
Mental/oral starter	Mental Warm-up Activities *(Practise a necessary pre-requisite skill)*	Mental Warm-up Activities *(Rehearse number bonds)*	Mental Warm-up Activities *(Play a 'bingo' game)*
Main teaching activity	1. Teacher card front *(Introduce topic to whole class)* 2. Activity Book and number grids *(Brief practice activity)*	1. Teacher card front and first activity (whole class) *(Rehearse the main teaching point)* 2. Activities from the Activity Book, Workbooks or Photocopy Masters *(Children work in four groups)*	1. Teacher card back *(Rehearse the main teaching point, using different model)* 2. Workbook and/or Activity book *(Children work in pairs and individually on a graded task)* 3. Assessment book *(Assess children's work)*
Plenary	Teacher card back *(Rehearse the main point and play a game)*	Teacher card back *(Address some common difficulties)*	Teacher card back *(Rehearse main teaching point through common difficulty)*

Supporting teachers in teaching and children in learning

Abacus is founded on the idea that teachers need to be in control of how and when they teach a particular piece of mathematics to their class. It is the teacher, and not the materials, which make the professional decisions. Therefore the Abacus materials have been designed to allow you to decide:

- how long to spend on any one topic;
- how to structure that topic – the proportion of time spent on whole class teaching, group work, individual or paired practice, assessment and revision;
- how to time the different parts of the lesson – the length of mental/oral sections, direct teaching, practice;
- the order in which to teach the topics;
- how to relate the teaching of number and non-number topics.

Flexibility in the teaching of each topic

Whilst the Abacus planning grids (from page 41) have been designed to match the medium term planning grids in the Numeracy Framework, a degree of flexibility is nevertheless built in. Abacus allows you to structure each topic as you see fit. Some topics may be completed in two days, and some will run over three days, and it is up to you how long to remain on any one topic. In Abacus, as in the Framework, there is often a sequence of related topics, and the practice of some of the key skills may therefore continue over two, or even three, topics. This allows for the maximum reinforcement of the basic skills and facts.

Flexibility in classroom management

The basic Abacus model enables you to decide how best to structure the main teaching activity. Each Teacher Card is structured to provide a minimum of two whole class teaching sessions, drawing upon different models or images in demonstrating the topic to the children. The Activity Book supplies a variety of activities, from those for use with the whole class to those directed at small groups or pairs. The Workbooks and Photocopy Masters allow for structured and appropriate levels of practice, and again these can be used individually or in pairs, or to structure some group work.

Teaching in classes with three-term entry

The order of the Abacus Teacher Cards matches closely the order of topics outlined in the medium term planning grids in the Numeracy Framework. This means that there is a planned overlap in the order of topics from term to term. It is therefore quite possible to plan and teach a topic to two or more groups, moving across from one set of objectives to another.

With Abacus, the organisation of this becomes quite simple. You select the appropriate Teacher Cards from each term, e.g. autumn and spring. The pre-requisite skills for these cards will then allow you to select a mental/oral activity which can be carried out with the whole class (from the Mental Warm-up Activities). You can then move on to some direct teaching with one group following the selected Teacher Card, whilst the other group work on a practical activity. Later, or on the second day, it will be possible to move on to some direct teaching with the second group, from the appropriate Teacher Card, whilst the first group are engaged in relevant follow-up work.

Starting the lesson

As we know, the way a lesson starts can often dictate the direction of subsequent teaching. If a lesson gets off to a crisp, clear start, the children are likely to be well prepared to engage with the main topic being taught. The National Numeracy Strategy suggests that the first ten minutes of the lesson should be allocated to the practice and reinforcement of those skills and facts which benefit from a 'little and often' approach. In this category are included:

- counting in steps of different sizes, both forwards and backwards
- instant recall of number facts, including discussing ways of remembering the facts that need to be learned by heart
- previously-taught mental strategies.

It is not appropriate to introduce topics for the first time in this mental/oral part of the lesson, and neither should complex operations be explained. It is a time for 'quick-fire' rehearsal of basic skills, for using a strategy that has already been taught, or for choosing an operation to solve a problem quickly.

This part of the session will almost always be number work, although occasionally it may focus on a particular aspect of shape or of measures, such as 'time'. Importantly, it is not necessarily related to the second part of the lesson. For example, a teacher planning a lesson on 2-d shape could (and often would) include a starter activity on number.

This part of the lesson involves working with the whole class and only exceptionally would it be necessary to work with a group or to exempt individuals from the session. The Abacus Mental Warm-up Activities have been specifically written to address this part of the lesson, and provide a wide variety of whole class oral and mental activities for each day's teaching.

Main teaching activity

The function of the main part of the lesson can vary, depending upon various factors (where you are in a topic, the age and maturity of the children etc.). It can provide time for:

● introducing a new topic;
● extending previous work and developing children's understanding;
● practising a skill or strategy;
● using and applying what has been learned;
● assessing children's learning;
● revising or revisiting a topic.

During the main teaching activity, the teacher can choose how to organise the class. It is quite possible that the lesson you teach on a Monday will have quite a different style of classroom organisation from the lesson you teach on Tuesday. Clearly, the way you choose to organise the class will be guided by the purpose of the lesson (is it introducing a new topic, or rehearsing an old one?). It will also dictate, to some extent, the teaching strategy you use. For example, a whole class lesson could require a higher percentage of demonstration or explanation, whilst a lesson where groups of children are working together could involve more discussion or description. Taking all these factors into account, on any one day a teacher can choose to organise the class:

● as a whole class session, with direct teaching of the whole class or with a paired investigation;
● with the children working in groups, and the teacher working in a focused way with one or two of the groups;
● with the children working on a task in pairs or as individuals.

Although the Numeracy Strategy explicitly encourages a flexible approach to the organisation of the main teaching activity, it is clear about three central points:

● the need for teachers to organise the class to fit the purpose of the lesson
● that, although any one lesson may not involve a high proportion of direct teaching of the whole class (or year group) nevertheless, over the complete unit, more than 50% of the teaching is likely to be of this form
● that emphasis should be placed on keeping the children together, so it would not be appropriate to set more than three levels of work for any one year group, and no more than two levels of work per year group in a mixed-age range class (though, clearly, specific provision must be made for particular children who have individual education plans).

It is clear (both from the final report of the Numeracy Task Force, and the National Numeracy Strategy itself) that at the heart of the teaching and learning process is the active, direct teaching of a topic. In order to focus on this, teachers need to have:

- a clear objective for each lesson and a set of objectives for the topic
- a definite 'way of teaching' – an image or model (e.g. number line, money) which will be used to represent or demonstrate the mathematics
- a variety of teaching strategies to ensure that the lesson is interactive.

The Abacus Teacher Cards have been designed with these three requirements in mind.

- They provide a clear set of objectives for each unit, with specific learning objectives for each activity.
- They outline the model to be used in teaching the mathematics, and make clear the careful use of vocabulary.
- They also provide a variety of teaching strategies, through the work with the whole class, the group activities, the individual and paired practice and the extra support provided by the Simmering Activities and the Infant Games.

The plenary session

Plenary sessions can often be the hardest part of the lesson to teach successfully. The children (and the teacher!) are tired, and some will require more feedback than others meaning that boredom may cause disruption. It is hard to plan the plenary session because it will often develop from what has occurred during the lesson.

The purpose of the plenary as explained by the Numeracy Strategy is threefold. It allows time for:

- A rehearsal of the main teaching points and summary of the key facts. This is the vital, 'What have we learned today?' part of the lesson.
- Children to present their work to you and others, particularly those who may have been working independently during the main part of the lesson.
- Addressing any difficulties that may have arisen during the lesson.
- Forward planning – helping to make explicit what we are going to do next, and perhaps outlining any homework.

Rehearsing the main teaching points of the lesson is very important for two reasons. Firstly, it allows you to ensure that the learning objectives have been clearly articulated and that children have taken this in. Secondly, it enables you to pick up any difficulties that several children may have shared. Frequently there will be common misconceptions or errors which it can prove useful to address with the whole class. This is not to point out children who have made mistakes, but rather to use common errors as a way of rehearsing the teaching points.

The Abacus Teacher Cards highlight the key learning points and also provide advice on probable common misconceptions which may occur when teaching that particular topic. This will allow you to plan how to address such misconceptions, as well as preparing you to look out for difficulties which are encountered by several children.

Taking feedback from children is difficult to do in a way which does not leave some of the class feeling bored or frustrated. It helps to vary the format of their presentation. For example:

- ask some children to write the hardest or easiest question they had to do on the board
- give some children a poster or a strip of paper to record some or all of their work during an activity, so that they can display this
- ask a group to show their work and then choose a question to ask the rest of the class
- choose a pair of children to demonstrate a strategy they have been using
- choose some children to write the answer to a question on the board. The rest of the class have to guess what the question was.

The plenary can also be made easier by discussing a group of children's work with them, and then marking it together just before you bring the whole class together. That group can then show the children their work by showing any pieces you felt were particularly special.

The plenary should end with a suggestion about where the children are going next in mathematics. You may be going to extend the work you did today, or start a new topic. Sometimes you will want to give the class an informal homework activity (e.g. *look out for car numbers that end in '5'. Can you remember one to tell me tomorrow?*).

The plenary should be kept short – a protracted ending will not improve the lesson or make the children learn any more. The lesson needs to be brought to a sharp close, and the plenary enables the teacher to evaluate its success.

Homework

In reception, formal homework is inappropriate. The involvement of parents, however, is as important as ever. If parents are encouraged to become involved in their children's learning at this stage, they are likely to stay involved over the next few years and the benefits to children's achievements will be enormous. The primary purposes of homework include:

- involving parents in their children's learning
- helping parents keep abreast of what the child can and cannot do
- encouraging parents and children to talk about their maths and what they are learning.

These processes all start in the early years, and in children's first year at school we set up patterns of co-operation.

In reception, we can ask children to share parts of their mathematical learning with their parents. All parents can be encouraged to count with their children, and to help them to recognise numbers. Make a tape of the children counting as a whole class, and let different children borrow it to take home. Children are naturally proud of their achievements and sharing these with their parents is very important. Encourage parents to play card and board games with their child, and perhaps allow children to take home maths games. Encourage parents to make a 'personalised' number line for their child or make them in class to take home.

It is also possible to encourage children to undertake informal maths tasks at home. These would normally not be written activities, but would include activities such as looking at a handful of coins and noticing which coin is the largest, or finding a car number-plate that has the digit '2' in it. Children often enjoy carrying out a piece of informal 'homework' at home and discussing the maths involved with their parents.

Many schools use shared maths activities and games as the basis for parental involvement in maths. The activities on the back of the Teacher Cards can be modified for this purpose.

Assessment

Opportunities for informal assessment occur throughout many of the aspects of an Abacus unit.

The Mental Warm-up Activities offer opportunities for observational assessment, both for the whole class and for individuals. The continuous feedback in the form of child response to these tasks provides immediate observational measures of performance. The opportunities in this stage of the unit for you to set tasks for varying levels of ability informs further when assessing the feedback.

Similarly, during the Plenary sessions, observational assessment opportunities are numerous.

Additional opportunities are provided during the main teaching, both during the interactive element of the teaching, and particularly when the children are engaged in group activities, and you are focusing on a chosen group.

Assessment of the children's' written work is provided from completed Workbook pages and Photocopy Masters and can be recorded using the Assessment grids on pages 36 and 37.

⑥ Differentiation

The National Numeracy Strategy emphasises the need to keep the children together. This links to the requirement that, over a period of time, the proportion of whole class direct teaching should be more than 50% (indeed, it is easy to see how this figure could be closer to 75% in a single year group, given that the mental starter and plenary both involve working with the whole class).

Whole class focus

Although any one lesson may not involve a high proportion of whole class direct teaching, over a complete topic, more than 50% of the teaching is likely to be with the whole class.

Keeping the children together

Emphasis should be placed on keeping the children together, so that it would not be appropriate to set more than three levels of work for any one year group, and no more than two levels of work per year group in a mixed-age class. Clearly, specific provision must be made for particular children who have individual education plans.

This marks a change in attitude to teaching the class, and has repercussions for record-keeping and assessment plans. Given that we are now:
● teaching the same topic to all the children
● practising pre-requisite skills in the mental/oral starter with all the children
● dividing into no more than three groups for the main part of the lesson
it is no longer necessary to write notes on the progress of every single child. The majority of each year group will be engaged in the same tasks, and studying the same mathematics at the same level. For these children, it is important to record deviations from the norm; i.e. what happens if the child was not able to cope with the work given, or if they found it too easy.

It remains as true as ever that children are individuals, who do not all learn or develop at the same rate. The following points may help teachers to cope with the inevitable differences between children when they are teaching the whole class and 'keeping all the children together'.

It is important to remember that the class may be divided into more than three groups as long as there are no more than three levels of work. Most teachers organise their class so that the children are seated in small groups. They may, therefore, have two or three 'tables' working at the same level, probably on the same activity. One or two more, or less able children may be working on an activity more appropriate for their ability.

Once the topic has been introduced to the children, and the main direct teaching has taken place, it is usual to split the class into groups for most of them to work more independently, and to practise or apply what they have just been taught. It is only in this way that children come to make this knowledge their own. It is also the means of finding out who has, and who has not, grasped the mathematics, and therefore assessing the need for further teaching or practice. It is a sensible strategy to work with the children who need most help first, since this is the group who are likely to need some further teaching before they are able to work independently or semi-independently on the topic.

There is (as the Numeracy Strategy makes clear) a 'hierarchy' of types of work which can be used when planning for groups of children. It is easiest for children to do work which has been laid out for them, and where few decisions have to be made about what is to be done. Thus Workbooks, or Photocopy Masters, are relatively simple for children to use independently from the teacher. Work written on the board is more difficult, since children must lay it out for themselves. Activities involving structural materials, coins, number cards, grids, etc. can require quite a high input from the teacher.

Abacus provides materials for the different levels of work suggested by the Numeracy Strategy and also helps to organise the class so that you are working in a focused way with one group, as recommended. The Activity Book indicates activities targeted at three ability levels, and the Workbooks allow for children who find the work moderately easy to engage, with extension activities. It is easiest to organise the class so that those children who are working relatively independently have suitably contained activities – (e.g. Workbooks, Photocopy Masters), whilst those children who have the benefit of your focused attention engage in the activities which enable further directed teaching.

Special needs

Children who have Individual Education Plans (IEPs) will normally be included in the whole class parts of the lesson, such as the mental/oral starter, the plenary, and the introduction to the topic in the main teaching activity. It will be rare for a child to be excluded from these parts of the lesson, although behaviour management, or their skills level may mean that they are only present for some of these activities. Once a topic has been introduced, the teacher will need to ensure that the follow-up activities are at a level which is appropriate for the child and which fit with their development plan. Normally children with IEPs will work on the same topic as the remainder of the class, but at a lower level or by addressing some of the pre-requisite skills needed to engage with that topic. This work can be selected either from the Abacus unit itself, drawing upon appropriate activities, or from related Units covered earlier.

7 Teaching strategies

Abacus is conceived around the conviction that active teaching is at the heart of an effective mathematics lesson. Although most teachers never analyse what they do, teaching in fact includes a number of different components. Good, lively and direct teaching involves:

- demonstrating or modelling a strategy or skill. This can include showing children how to do something or providing an image to help them to understand a strategy;
- instructing, or talking children through a procedure or process to be followed;
- explaining and illustrating - providing reasons and giving examples;
- questioning and discussing, so that teachers actively encourage children's engagement with mathematics;
- practising, rehearsing and reinforcing a skill or a set of operations. Teachers use repetition to increase familiarity, and practice to help consolidation of strategies or procedures;
- evaluating children's responses and dealing with errors.

In order to teach a good lesson, you need to have a clear sense of **what** they are teaching and **how** to teach it, using a set of strategies. This means knowing which images or resources can be used to demonstrate or model a particular mathematical concept or operation. The Abacus Teacher Cards outline the objectives clearly, so that you know precisely what is being covered in each Unit. It can be a good idea to share a key objective with the children, often writing it at the top of the flipchart or board. *Today, we are going to learn how to count back from 20.*

The Teacher Card also describes the images or models which can be used to teach each topic effectively (the Abacus authors have brought a great deal of expertise and effort to bear in this area). Teachers can be confident of having a range of ways to represent or demonstrate the mathematics involved, to enable children to understand and apply what they are learning.

When teaching children from 4 to 7 years old, it is almost always possible to break down the representation of a piece of mathematics into two stages. First, children need a model – a way of understanding the appropriate mathematical concept. Second, they need to be shown how to perform the operation involved.

For example, when beginning to teach addition we want children to understand that addition is not only about combining two sets of objects, but also about counting on along a number line. So, 5 + 2 can be modelled by adding two bricks to a tower of five (making it more likely that children will count on from '5', rather than counting the bricks in the first tower). Addition will also be modelled using a number line or track, starting from 5 and counting on two more. The towers and the number line both provide a representation of the mathematics involved. They enable children to make sense of what they are being taught and to hold visual images in their heads.

However, children also need a practical and easy way of doing any appropriate additions. In this example, they will almost certainly be taught how to use fingers to count on when performing additions (relating back to the model, e.g. the number line). *Start at 5 and count on two more, using fingers. Six, seven. The answer is seven.* The demonstration or modelling uses the towers of bricks or the number line, but the method of doing the additions will use fingers.

Abacus draws upon a wide variety of models, images and strategies to demonstrate and explain the mathematical concepts and operations which children encounter in their first three years at school. These include:
- number lines 1 to 20, and beyond
- number grids (0 to 99 or 1 to 100)
- small digit cards
- towers and large bricks
- interlocking cubes in sets of ten, and loose cubes
- place-value cards
- money, particularly 10p coins and 1p coins to help with place-value
- a coat-hanger with key rings or pegs attached
- toys and role-play (shopping, giving change, etc.).

In addition, Abacus develops a number of effective and pragmatic strategies for children to use when performing mathematical operations, such as adding two numbers. These include:
- fingers – used to help count, count on or back, double numbers, learn number pairs for numbers up to and including ten, count in twos, fives and tens, and recognise odd and even numbers;
- number lines or tracks – used to help count on, find a difference, count back, compare numbers, round to the nearest multiple of ten;
- number grids (0 to 99 or 1 to 100) – used to help count to 100, add or subtract tens or multiples of ten, count in steps of various sizes, compare numbers or to find the next multiple of ten;
- place-value cards – used to help compare numbers and understand the value of each digit.

Questioning

There are two types of question which are used in teaching – open questions and closed questions. Open questions are generally addressed to the whole class. Closed questions can be targeted at particular children (though they too can be addressed to a large group). You need to consider which type of question is most likely to achieve the response you require, as well as which will serve the mathematical end you have in mind. It is often true that a question asked in an 'open' form will achieve a much higher degree of interaction than the same question if asked in a closed format. For example, a closed question might be: *What adds to 3 to make 10?* whereas a more open question would be: *Who can tell me two numbers which add together to make 10?* The first question has only one answer, but the second can be used to generate a response from every pair of children in the room.

How do you expect the children to respond to your questions?

The traditional mode of teacher question and pupil answer, where children wave their hands in the air and one child is selected to answer, can result in frustrated children and only a few of the class taking part. Recent trials show that teachers are increasingly drawing on a range of resources to encourage all the children in the class to respond to a question. The children can:

- use number cards, holding these up to show an answer
- all suggest answers, so that the teacher then records lots of different answers on the flipchart or board and then rehearses the operation with the class to see which answer is correct
- keep an answer hidden and then reveal it on a count of three
- all say or shout an answer in unison – particularly where an answer which you hope is on 'automatic pilot' is required, such as: *Four and what make ten?*
- work in pairs to write down an answer, and then hand in papers (without names on).

We know, from the evidence of both research and practice over recent years, that questions and answers can provide a valuable means of creating an interactive teaching environment. One useful strategy is to give each child a 'maths partner' to work with in short bursts in question and answer sessions, or when playing whole class games. The first time the class work with their pairs may prove difficult, but they will soon start working well together and you will notice great improvements in their speaking and listening.

8 Specific guidance on mathematical content

In order to get the best out of the Abacus materials, you are advised to note the following points.

Counting

It is important that the sequence and naming structure of the number system becomes second nature to the children. Abacus encourages frequent practice at reciting numbers in sequence in a variety of different ways, with particular emphasis on counting in ones and in tens.
The number line and a number grid (0 to 99 or 1 to 100) are frequently used as models, and children are encouraged to use their fingers to enhance the development of their counting skills.

Addition and subtraction

Abacus places strong emphasis on the development of children's mental addition and subtraction skills, and children are taught a variety of strategies to enhance this development. The emphasis placed on reciting numbers in sequence, lays the foundation for using the strategies of counting on and counting back to add and subtract. The number line and the 1 to 100 number square are frequently used to model both addition and subtraction.

Many mental addition and subtraction skills depend on a sound knowledge of addition pairs (or bonds) to 10, to 20, to 100, for example. Abacus places a great emphasis on the recognition of addition pairs to 10 in Key Stage 1. This means more than knowing that, for example, 3 and 7 make 10 and includes the child being able to respond immediately with one member of the 'pair', when hearing the other.

Abacus encourages a careful structured development in the use of appropriate vocabulary associated with addition and subtraction. The long term aim is for children to recognise all the different ways of reading the '+' and '−' signs, and the '=' sign. The vocabulary suggested on the Teacher Cards has a development with this aim in view.

Money

Abacus uses money to provide a 'real life' and familiar context within which to locate many numerical operations and concepts. Children are encouraged to see 'hundreds, tens and units' in terms of pound coins, ten pence pieces and one pence pieces. All children will regard money and coins as both interesting and important. Its use as a structured model for place-value benefits from this interest.

Children see adults using, enjoying and worrying about money. They are well aware of the importance accorded to money in our society. They know that money transactions are an essential part of our daily lives. Unlike coloured bricks, blocks or interlocking cubes, money has an importance and a reality outside the primary classroom. It is this fact that makes money such a powerful teaching tool. Children want to operate using money. They want to understand how money works, and to participate in the 'adult' transactions that they see around them.

Measures

In all aspects of measures (e.g. length, weight, capacity, angle), Abacus provides pupils with activities which develop the important skill of estimation. Providing children with estimating experiences enhances their understanding of the measurement concepts involved.

Weight and mass

Throughout this stage of work in Abacus the work 'weight' is used in preference to 'mass'. Scientifically, the weight is the force exerted by the earth's gravitational field on an object: weight can then be crudely interpreted as the pull towards the ground. The mass of an object is the quantity of matter it contains. The force of attraction varies with the position of the object, but the quantity of matter remains fixed. So, for example, an astronaut weighs less on the Moon because the Moon's gravitational attraction is weaker than the Earth's. The astronaut's mass – the amount of matter in his body – is unchanged.

The weight of an object can be found by using a spring balance, bathroom scale or direct-reading kitchen scale, but the mass has to be found by using balance scales where an object is placed in one pan and a balance obtained by placing objects of known mass in the other.

Though this distinction between weight and mass is clear to the scientist, it is rarely made in daily life. Later in Abacus, when units have been developed and understood, this distinction will be relatively easy to grasp, but at this stage the word weight is used in accordance with its everyday usage. If you are concerned about this decision, the word mass may be used when it is obviously more appropriate, but the intention is that no undue worry should be centred around the distinction between the two words.

9. Framework for teaching mathematics matching chart

Counting and recognising numbers

Counting

Say and use the number names in order in familiar contexts such as number rhymes, songs, stories, counting games and activities (first to five, then ten, then twenty and beyond).	Warm-ups
Recite the number names in order, continuing the count forwards or backwards from a given number.	N1, N2, N6, N7, N8
Count reliably up to 10 everyday objects (first to 5, then 10, then beyond), giving just one number name to each object. Recognise small numbers without counting.	N2, N10, N18
Begin to recognise 'none' and 'zero' in stories, rhymes and when counting.	Warm-ups
Count reliably in other contexts, such as clapping sounds or hopping movements.	N7, N15
Count in tens.	N23, Warm-ups
Count in twos.	Warm-ups
Estimate a number in the range that can be counted reliably, then check by counting.	N10, N18, N23

Reading and writing numbers

Recognise numerals 1 to 9, then 0 and 10, then beyond 10.	N1, N2, N10, N17
Begin to record numbers, initially by making marks, progressing to simple tallying and writing numerals.	N2, N8, N10, N17, N18

Comparing and ordering numbers

Use language such as more or less, greater or smaller, to compare two numbers and say which is more or less, and say a number which lies between two given numbers.	N3, N5, N14, N17, N21
Order a given set of numbers: for example, the set of numbers 1 to 6 given in random order.	N5, N14, N21
Order a given set of selected numbers: for example, the set 2, 5, 1, 8, 4	Warm-ups
Begin to understand and use ordinal numbers in different contexts.	Warm-ups

Adding and subtracting

Adding and subtracting

In practical activities and discussion:

Begin to use the vocabulary involved in adding and subtracting	N3, N11, N16
Find one more or one less than a number from 1 to 9.	N3, N11, N19
Begin to relate addition to combining two groups of objects, counting all the objects; extend to three groups of objects.	N4, N12
Begin to relate addition to counting on.	N3, N19, N22
Begin to relate the addition of doubles to counting on.	N19, N22
Find a total by counting on when on group of objects is hidden.	N3, N12, N22
Separate (partition) a given number of objects into two groups.	N22
Select two groups of objects to make a given total.	N22, N24
Begin to relate subtraction to 'taking away' and counting how many are left.	N6, N16
Remove a smaller number from a larger and find how many are left by counting back from the larger number.	N19, N24
Begin to find out how many have been removed from a larger group of objects by counting up from a number.	N24
Work out by counting how many more are needed to make a larger number.	N19, N24

* Key objectives are highlighted in **bold type.**

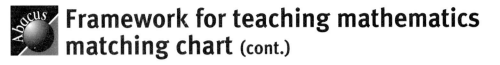

Solving problems

Reasoning about numbers or shapes

Talk about, recognise and recreate simple patterns: for example, simple repeating or symmetrical patterns from different cultures.	Children are encouraged, and given opportunities to reason about numbers and shapes throughout the Abacus materials
Solve simple problems or puzzles in a practical context, and respond to 'What could we try next?'	
Make simple estimates and predictions: for example, of the number of cubes that will fit in a box or strides across the room.	
Sort and match objects, pictures or children themselves, justifying the decisions made.	

Problems involving 'real life' or money

Use developing mathematical ideas and methods to solve practical problems involving counting and comparing in a real or role play context.	Warm-ups
Begin to understand and use the vocabulary related to money. Sort coins, including the £1 and £2 coins, and use them in role play to pay and give change.	N8, N13, N20

Measures, shape and space

Comparing and ordering measures

Use language such as more or less, longer or shorter, heavier or lighter ... to compare two quantities, then more than two, by making direct comparisons of lengths or masses, and by filling and emptying containers.	M1, M2, M4, M5, M7, M8
Begin to understand and use the vocabulary of time.	M3, M6, M9
Sequence familiar events.	M3, M6, M9
Begin to know the days of the week in order.	M9
Begin to read o'clock time.	M6

Exploring pattern, shape and space

Use language such as circle or bigger to describe the shape and size of solids and flat shapes.	S1, S2, S5, S6
Begin to name solids such as a cube, cone, sphere ... and flat shapes such as circle, triangle, square, rectangle ... Use a variety of shapes to make models, pictures and patterns, and describe them.	S1, S2, S5, S6
Put sets of objects in order of size.	M1, M2, M4, M7, M8
Talk about, recognise and recreate patterns: for example, simple repeating or symmetrical patterns in the environment (see also Reasoning).	Warm-ups
Use everyday works to describe position, direction and movement for example, follow and give instructions about positions, directions and movements in PE and other activities.	S3, S4

* Key objectives are highlighted in **bold type**.

⑩ Classroom materials

Materials provided in the *Resource Bank*

Number line (0 to 20) – large, double-sided, full-colour number cards, for demonstration

Number line (0 to 100) – medium, double-sided two-colour number cards, for demonstration

Class pack of small number cards (0 to 10) – 30 sets, for individual children

Group pack of small number cards (0 to 10) – 10 sets for group work

Group pack of small number cards (0 to 30) – 5 sets for group work

Pack of small number cards (0 to 100) – 1 set for group work

Wall chart pack (0 to 99 grid and 1 to 100 grid) – 6 sets for a school

Place-value cards (standard pack) – 5 sets of units, tens and hundreds

Place-value cards (extended pack) – 5 sets of units, tens, hundreds, thousands, tenths and hundredths

Other specialised resources, such as small number grids and number tracks are included as Photocopy Masters in the Activity Book.

Infant Games pack

24 games referenced to specific Teacher Card units.

Assumed mathematical materials in the classroom

Interlocking cubes

Counters

Spotty dice (1 to 6)

Numbered dice (1 to 6) and
  (0 to 5) and (1 to 10)

Calculators

Dominoes

Playing cards

Coins (real and plastic)

Base Ten equipment

Sets of plastic 2-d shapes

Sets of solid 3-d shapes

Containers (for Capacity)

Analogue clock with moveable hands

Digital clock

Sand timers or rocking timers

Seconds timer or stopclock

Weighing balances

Weighing scales

Sets of weights

Rulers/metre sticks/tape measures

Centicubes

Pegboards and pegs

Other materials

Washing line with pegs attached

Hoops

Cloth (Feely) bags

Blu-tack

Soft toys

Construction equipment

Coat-hanger and keyrings

⑪ Assessment grid (Key Stage 1)

To assist with statutory assessment, selected items from the level descriptions are included within the scheme. For each item, key stages within the scheme are identified. This gives you a quick reference for reporting progress. Each item is presented in the form:

I can...

> read, write, count and order numbers up to 10.
>
>
> Abacus R N5, N8, N14

You can then quickly assess achievement using an on/off principle. The child **can do** or **cannot do**. There are no interim stages on the records.

● The system allows a cumulative record to develop.
● Each box can be completed in a variety of ways:
  – a simple tick or colouring in by you or pupil;
  – a colouring in using a different colour for each year: red for Reception, blue for Year 1, green for Year 2, ... yellow for Year 6;
  – or preferably a short comment on a particular child's attainment.

At the bottom of each box is a code showing where to check this particular statement (of the form Abacus R N5 – Abacus Reception Unit N5, or Abacus 1 N8 – Abacus 1 Unit N8 etc.). In some instances this will be at different stages within the scheme to match the development of individual children. Your observations during mental warm-ups, focused group work, or written evidence from Workbooks and Assessment sheets will provide plenty of evidence of achievement for each statement. The record sheets can also be used as:

● a prompt at the planning stage
● part of a record of achievement
● a tool for feeding back to parents
● a check of a child's individual progress
● an assessment of group or whole class progress.

The items included within the assessment grid are taken from the appropriate level descriptions of each attainment target in the National Curriculum. You will be able to use the cumulative information contained within the grid, together with your global view of the child's progress and any other factors you think appropriate, in coming to a decision about whether the child has successfully achieved the appropriate level within each attainment target.

There is no suggestion that the grid alone will provide the only evidence for making end of year or end of key stage assessments. Abacus is in full accord with the objectives in the National Curriculum in wanting these decisions to be based on the level description as a whole rather than simply a collection of disparate items.

 **Assessment grid: Key Stage 1**
Number

Name_____

I can …

Level 1	Level 2	Level 3
read, write, count and order numbers up to 10. Abacus R N5, N8, N14	read, write, count and order numbers up to 100. Abacus 1 N15	read, write, count and order numbers up to 1000. Abacus 2 N34
add and subtract with totals up to 10. Abacus R N19, N22	understand place-value in numbers to 100. Abacus 1 N9, N16 Abacus 2 N2, N16	understand and use place-value in numbers to 1000. Abacus 2 N36
know one more or less than a number (up to 10). Abacus R N3, N6	use mental recall of addition and subtraction facts to 10. Abacus 1 N11, N14, N18 Abacus 2 N3	use mental recall of addition and subtraction facts to 20. Abacus 2 N18, N31
recognise and make repeating patterns. Abacus 1 N22	know one or ten more/less than a number (up to 30). Abacus 1 N12, N28, N29	mentally recall the ×2, ×3, ×4, ×5 and ×10 multiplication tables and associated division facts. *Abacus 3* Abacus 2 N12, N13, N25, N39
	recognise sequences of numbers, including odd and even. Abacus 1 N8, N21, N34 Abacus 2 N7	use mental strategies to add and subtract numbers with two digits. Abacus 2 N6, N33 *Abacus 3*

Assessment grid: Key Stage 1
Shape, Space and Measures

Name_____

I can ...

Level 1	Level 2	Level 3
use everyday language to describe properties of 2-d and 3-d shapes. Abacus R S1, S2	use mathematical language to describe 2-d and 3-d shapes and their properties. Abacus 1 S1, S3	classify 2-d and 3-d shapes using mathematical properties. Abacus 1 S4, S5 Abacus 2 S1, S4
measure and order objects by direct comparison. Abacus R M1, M2, M4, M5, M7, M8	use mathematical language to describe position, direction and movement. Abacus 1 S2, S6	recognise and use reflective symmetry. Abacus 1 S7 Abacus 2 S6
order events. Abacus R M6, M9	use standard and non-standard units to measure length and mass. Abacus 1 M2, M6	use non-standard and standard metric units of length, capacity, weight and time. Abacus 1 M2, M6 Abacus 2 M2, M5, M6, M10, M11

⑫ Getting started with Abacus

Making a number line

The image of a line of numbers is a very powerful assistance to children in helping them to perform number operations and develop an understanding of how the number system works. Abacus makes use of number cards pegged onto a washing line. The easiest way to make this line – which can remain hanging up in the classroom throughout the year – is as follows:

(i)   You will need a length of thickish string, some pegs and some matchsticks.

(ii) Thread the required number of pegs (ten to start with and then twenty later in the year) onto the string. Do not clip the pegs on in the usual way. Thread the string through the small horizontal round hole in the middle of the metal spring in the peg. The pegs will then remain attached to the string while cards are clipped in and out of them.

(iii) Put a small piece of matchstick in through each hole to wedge the string firm. This stops the pegs sliding along the string. They can still be opened and shut to hold cards in the usual way.

(iv) Clip on the number cards (provided in the Resource Bank).

This number line makes an immensely powerful resource in the classroom. It is useful to have a permanent number line up around the walls of the classroom with numbers up to 30, and then as the year progresses, with the numbers up to 100 added. This means that the children can look at this 'visual aid' to help them with their work. It also provides the powerful image of the sequence of numbers which we wish them to internalise.

Have a smaller number line on hand to use for all the activities and lessons where it is mentioned in Abacus. This number line should also be permanently displayed and can be used for a quick 'early' mathematics activity each day. Swap two numbers around. Can the children say which two have been swapped? Remove one number. Which one is missing? Turn one number back to front, e.g. 15 becomes 51. Can the children say which number in the sequence is no longer correct?

Introducing Abacus

Abacus may be introduced to a whole school at once, or it may be started with a class of pupils who have come from other schools, and who have not previously been working with the Abacus approach.

Many children will bring number skills with them when they enter the school at Reception. The key skills to develop and consolidate here are:

- saying the number names to 10;
- recognising the numerals from 1 to 9.

⓭ Planning

The heart of good teaching is understanding the relationship between **what** is taught and **how** best to teach it. The plan is your way of making this connection explicit. In order to be an effective (even excellent) teacher, it is not necessary to spend hours planning. Indeed, sometimes overplanning can be counter-productive. It is necessary to have:

- **Long term plans**, which enable each teacher to know that the pre-requisite skills and strategies needed for a particular piece of mathematics have been covered in previous years.
- **Medium term plans**, which enable each teacher to pace the content coverage over the course of the year, and also to give the appropriate weightings to each part of the curriculum.
- **Short term plans,** which enable each teacher to know exactly what they are teaching, and how they are teaching it, at the start of the topic.

The National Numeracy Strategy states that it is not necessary for teachers to draw up daily lesson plans, providing that the weekly plan has sufficient structure, content and classroom management information.

Long term planning

Any long term plan is now effectively supplied by the Framework for Teaching Mathematics. This outlines the key objectives (and all the other teaching objectives) for each year of the primary curriculum. In very particular circumstances, such as those pertaining to some Special Schools, it may be necessary to adapt the Framework, but for most schools, it supplies an essential long term plan, which staff can use and become familiar with.

Medium term planning

The medium term plan can also be derived from the Framework for Teaching Mathematics. You can copy the Medium term planning grids from the Framework and use them to construct your own individual medium term plans. Exemplar planning grids, mapping the Abacus Teacher Cards and objectives on to the Framework structure are provided from page 41, at the back of this book.

Because of the flexibility of the Abacus Teacher Cards, it is quite easy for you to alter this order, and to adapt it to suit the needs of your own class. The lesson objectives are clearly stated on each Teacher Card and it is, therefore, simple to postpone a Unit, or to exchange one Unit with another, if so desired.

Using Abacus, the time spent on long term and medium term planning has been cut to an absolute minimum. The exemplar planning grids we provide will ensure that the teaching objectives in the Framework for Teaching Mathematics are covered, and that the order and balance of the topics is preserved.

Short term planning

Given the long and medium term planning, the short term planning becomes a relatively simple task. Each week, you select the appropriate Abacus resources for the Unit(s) to be covered, study the Teacher Card(s) noting the teaching objectives and the resources needed, decide how to balance Units (Teacher Cards) over the week and note the objectives for each day on your weekly plan. You should record the resources to be used, and the ways in which you plan to teach the topics concerned. This information is all clearly outlined on the Teacher Cards.

The format of the weekly plan may vary from school to school, although each school will need to have discussed this and to have agreed a common model. Many schools will choose to use the sample plan outline provided by the Numeracy Strategy training materials. Weekly plans can be brief, but will certainly be more detailed for Monday and Tuesday than for later in the week. Any weekly plan will need to incorporate the following information:

- Clear objectives for the mental/oral section. *[Appropriate Warm-up activity]*
- Clear objectives for the main teaching activity. *[Teacher Card, front]*
- Brief outline of the mental/oral activity. *[Appropriate Warm-up activity]*
- Brief outline of the main teaching activity specifying:
  – the model or image being used to teach this topic
  – the resources needed for the lesson
  – the organisation of the class (whole class, groups, paired work…).
  [all on Teacher Card]
- Indication of the teacher's focus. (group, individuals …)
- Outline of any differentiated activities. *[Teacher Card, back]*
- Key vocabulary, including key questions. *[Teacher Card]*
- Learning outcomes. *[Teacher Card, back]*
- Brief outline of possible points for the plenary. *[Teacher Card, back]*

It is therefore no exaggeration to say that all of this information can be obtained from the Abacus materials, in particular the Teacher Card and related resources for each Unit. You will need to study the Abacus resources which accompany each Unit and plan your week's lessons accordingly. The questions of classroom management which need to be noted on the plan can be decided in relation to the activities you select from the Activity Book (or the Games Pack) and also from the Workbook pages, Photocopy Masters, the Simmering Activities and Mental Warm-up Activities.

Once a detailed weekly plan has been drawn up, teachers will not need a lesson plan for each day. It is certainly true that, as the teaching progresses, the weekly plan will need to be modified and more detail added for the end of the week. However, this does not necessitate starting afresh, but rather adapting what has already been outlined.

Summary

The starting point for the weekly plan is the medium-term plan, which is drawn from the Framework (exemplars for Abacus are provided from page 41). The weekly plan needs to provide clear information about:

● what you are teaching – clear objectives for each part of the lesson each day;
● how you are teaching it – outline of the teaching in each part;
● how the class is to be managed – any differentiated activities and your focus each day;
● what the children have learned and how you will evaluate this.

Once you have a good weekly plan, daily lesson plans are unnecessary.

Within Abacus, all the necessary information to enable you to plan as above is available in a simple and unambiguous form on the Teacher Card for each Unit.

Planning grids

The tables on the following pages show one way of matching the Abacus Units to the Numeracy Framework Planning Grids. They are arranged termly.

You may wish to match the Abacus Units to the Planning Grids in a different order, or you may wish to use your own planning grids. Clearly, whichever order you use, your ongoing evaluation and assessment will inform the development of the scheme of work during the course of the year.

Exemplar planning grid: autumn

Note: In the grid, the Abacus Unit refers to the main teaching focus of the lesson. Mental and oral skills, such as counting, will be practised every day, using the Mental Warm-up Activities.

Unit	Topic	Abacus Unit	Teaching points	Notes
1	Counting	N1 Numbers to 10	To recite the number names in order to 20 To recite the number names in order, starting from a given number To say the number after a given number up to 6	
2	Counting	N2 Numbers to 10	To recite the number names in order to 20 To begin to count a set of objects up to 10, giving one number name to each object To begin to record numbers (up to 10)	
3	Shape and Space	S1 2-d shape	To recognise and name squares and circles To sort 2-d shapes according to shape	
4	Counting Measures	M1 Length	To compare the lengths of two objects directly To begin to understand the language associated with length	
		M2 Length	To compare the height of two objects directly To begin to understand the language associated with height	
5	Counting Adding (one more)	N3 Addition	To begin to understand the vocabulary of addition To add 'one' to a number up to 10 and recognise addition as counting on (one more) To find a total by counting on one when that object is hidden	
		N4 Addition	To begin to understand addition as combining two sets	
6	Assess and review			

Unit	Topic	Abacus Unit	Teaching points	Notes
7	Counting Comparing and ordering numbers	N5 Comparing	To compare two quantities using 'less than' and 'more than' To order numbers to 10	
8	Counting Adding and subtracting (one more, one less)	N6 Subtraction	To recite the number names in order from 1 to 20 and back To remove one object from a number and count the remainder	
9	Shape and space Reasoning	S2 3-d shape	To recognise and name cubes To begin to introduce the names of other 3-d shapes, e.g. cuboid To sort 3-d shapes	
10	Counting	N7 Numbers to 10	To recite the number names in order from 1 to 20 and back To count sounds and movements up to 10	
	Measures, including time	M3 Time	To understand the concept of measuring time To introduce the concept of a unit of time: one minute To count the number of times something occurs in a time period, using a sand timer	
11	Counting Money and 'real life' problems	N8 Numbers to 10	To recite the number names in order from 1 to 20 and back To read and begin to write numbers to 10 and beyond To begin to use the vocabulary of money	
12	Assess and review			

Exemplar planning grid: spring

Note: In the grid, the Abacus Unit refers to the main teaching focus of the lesson. Mental and oral skills, such as counting, will be practised every day, using the Mental Warm-up Activities.

Unit	Topic	Abacus Unit	Teaching points	Notes
1	Counting Comparing and ordering numbers	N9 Numbers to 15	To recite the number names in order to 20 and back To recite the number names in order, counting on from a given number To say the number 'after' a given number (up to 15)	
2	Counting Adding and subtracting	N10 Numbers to 20	To begin to count a set of objects up to 20, giving one number name to each object To begin to write numbers to 10 and beyond To begin to estimate small numbers of objects and to check	
3	Shape and space Reasoning	S3 Position	To begin to use the language of position	
4	Counting Measures	M4 Weight	To compare the weights of two objects by feel To compare the weights of two objects directly, using a balance scales To begin to understand the vocabulary associated with weight	
		M5 Capacity	To compare the capacities of two containers by pouring To begin to understand the vocabulary associated with capacity	
5	Counting Adding and subtracting Money and 'real life' problems	N11 Addition	To begin to understand the vocabulary of addition To add 1 or 2 to a number up to 10 and recognise addition as counting on (one/two more)	
		N12 Addition	To understand addition as combining two sets To find a total up to 10, by counting on, when the objects to be added are hidden	
6	Assess and review			

Unit	Topic	Abacus Unit	Teaching points	Notes
7	Counting and reading numbers Comparing and ordering numbers	N13 Counting and money	To recite the number names to 20 and beyond To begin to recognise coins (1p to £1)	
8	Counting and reading numbers Adding and subtracting	N14 Ordering	To compare two or three numbers, recognising the largest and smallest To order numbers to 10	
9	Shape and space Reasoning	S4 Direction	To begin to use the language of direction	
10	Counting and reading numbers	N15 Numbers to 20	To recite the number names to 20 and beyond To count sounds, objects and movements To count back from 20 to 1	
	Measures, including time	M6 Time	To recognise the hours on an analogue clock To read and set the time to the hour on an analogue clock To recognise key times of the day, e.g. nine o'clock – school starts	
11	Counting and reading numbers Adding and subtracting Money and 'real life' problems	N16 Subtraction	To remove two or three objects from a number and count the remainder To subtract by taking away	
12	Assess and review			

Exemplar planning grid: summer

Note: In the grid, the Abacus Unit refers to the main teaching focus of the lesson. Mental and oral skills, such as counting, will be practised every day, using the Mental Warm-up Activities.

Unit	Topic	Abacus Unit	Teaching points	Notes
1	Counting, reading and writing numbers Comparing and ordering numbers	N17 Numbers to 20	To recite the number names to 30 and beyond, stressing the fives To recite the number names in order from a given number To say the number before and after a given number To begin to write the numbers up to 20	
2	Counting, reading and writing numbers Adding and subtracting	N18 Numbers to 20	To recite the number names to 30 and beyond To count a set of objects up to 20 To estimate a number of objects and check by counting To write the numbers to 20	
3	Shape and space Reasoning	S5 Sorting 2-d shape	To sort 2-d shapes according to different properties To rehearse squares and circles To begin to name rectangles and triangles	
4	Counting, reading and writing numbers Measures	M7 Length	To understand the vocabulary associated with length To begin to measure length using a non-standard unit To begin to estimate length using non-standard units	
		M8 Length	To understand the vocabulary associated with length/height To begin to measure height using a non-standard unit To begin to estimate height using non-standard units	
5	Counting, reading and writing numbers Adding and subtracting Money and 'real life' problems	N19 Addition/ subtraction	To add or subtract one, from a number to 20 To understand addition as counting on To subtract, by counting back	
		N20 Counting and money	To recite the number names in order to 40 and beyond To recognise coins To solve simple addition and subtraction problems using money	
6	Assess and review			

Unit	Topic	Abacus Unit	Teaching points	Notes
7	Counting, reading and writing numbers Comparing and ordering numbers	N21 Ordering	To recognise a set of numbers more than or less than a given number (up to 20) To recognise the set of numbers between two others	
8	Counting, reading and writing numbers Adding and subtracting	N22 Addition	To understand addition as counting on (up to 12) To find the total, when the number to be added is hidden To partition a number of objects into two groups	
9	Shape and space Reasoning	S6 Sorting 3-d shape	To sort shapes according to whether or not they roll To recognise flat and curved faces on 3-d shapes To name cubes and cuboids To begin to name cones and pyramids	
10	Counting, reading and writing numbers	N23 Numbers to 100	To recite the number names to 30 and beyond To estimate a number of objects and check by counting To begin to count in tens to 100	
	Measures, including time	M9 Time	To recognise the names of the days of the week To order the days of the week To introduce 'tomorrow' and 'yesterday'	
11	Counting, reading and writing numbers Adding and subtracting Money and 'real life' problems	N24 Subtraction	To remove a small number of objects from a larger number To count back to see how many are left	
12	Assess and review			